UNIT WORKBOOK
for KENDLER'S
BASIC PSYCHOLOGY 2nd Ed

Jeffrey R. Corey

C. W. Post College

James S. McMichael

C. W. Post College

APPLETON-CENTURY-CROFTS
EDUCATIONAL DIVISION
New York **MEREDITH CORPORATION**

PRINTED IN THE UNITED STATES OF AMERICA
390-21118-4

CONTENTS

Unit		Kendler Pages	Page
1	Science and Behavior	3 - 25	1
2	Origins of Modern Psychology	29 - 47	5
3	Statistics	48 - 66	10
4	Biological Foundations	67 - 93	14
5	Vision I	97 - 115	21
6	Vision II	115 - 128	26
7	Audition and the Other Senses	128 - 143	31
8	Perception I	144 - 160	34
9	Perception II	160 - 186	39
10	Classical Conditioning	188 - 199	44
11	Instrumental Conditioning	199 - 214	49
12	Overview of Conditioning	214 - 231	55
13	Motivation I	233 - 258	59
14	Motivation II	258 - 276	64
15	Complex Instrumental Learning	281 - 300	68
16	Verbal and Motor Learning	300 - 326	73
17	Memory	328 - 347	77
18	Verbal Behavior	348 - 369	81
19	Cognitive Processes	370 - 402	85
20	Frustration	404 - 422	90
21	Conflict	422 - 444	94
22	Personality I	449 - 476	100
23	Personality II	476 - 497	105

24	Behavior Pathology I	499 - 511	110
25	Behavior Pathology II	511 - 530	115
26	Therapy	530 - 550	119
27	Social Behavior I	552 - 578	124
28	Social Behavior II	578 - 601	129
29	Psychological Tests	605 - 646	133
30	Applied Psychology	647 - 681	138

INTRODUCTION

This workbook consists of 30 units. For each unit there is a study outline relating to BASIC PSYCHOLOGY: SECOND EDITION by Howard H. Kendler (New York: Appleton-Century-Crofts, 1968). Each study outline gives objectives which provide an overview of study goals, the relevant pages in the textbook, terms to be defined and questions to be answered. How these study outlines can best be used will depend in part upon the structure of the course and the nature of the examination.

If the examinations consist primarily of multiple choice questions and the course structure focuses upon traditional classroom work, the student should take advantage of the STUDY GUIDE FOR HOWARD H. KENDLER'S BASIC PSYCHOLOGY: SECOND EDITION by Tracy S. Kendler (New York: Appleton-Century-Crofts, 1968). The use of this workbook along with the STUDY GUIDE would provide added emphasis to important points in the text.

If the course structure is based upon "personalized instruction", the material will be broken down into units which must be mastered in sequence. The study outlines in this workbook are designed to be particularly compatable with the personalized approach since each unit is short enough to be a single assignment and since the study outlines are designed to help in reaching Mastery of the material. The quizzes, which are provided to the instructor to accompany this workbook, sample widely the topics in the unit. However, these quizzes do not include items which do not appear on the study outlines. Therefore, a student who answers correctly all the questions on the study outline may expect to obtain a perfect score on the quiz. The system is designed to take the guesswork out of studying. Students who have participated in personalized instruction learn more about psychology and generally prefer the method to traditional lecture methods.*

In using this workbook the student should give answers to all the questions and should give answers which are as complete as possible. When defining terms the glossary in the back of the text is handy, but more thorough definitions along with examples and relationships among terms are found in the text itself. Completely filling out the study outline is also helpful to the instructor and his assistants if the student is having any difficulties, since sources of misunderstanding can be readily traced. Reverse pages have been left blank for the convenience of student note-taking.

*Our research on these issues was done under a grant from the Esso Education Foundation.

Objectives

Define the relevant terms on this study guide;
distinguish between independent and dependent variables. Be able to explain the different types of
independent variables. Distinguish between factual
and operational meaning. Understand the scientific
method and its relation to the science of psychology.

Define:

1. psychology _Science of behavior_

2. dependent variable _behavior in Psychology. Event that Psychologist seeks to understand_

3. independent variable _The factors responsible for the occurence of responses_

4. empirical _based on observation_

5. stimulus (plural = stimuli) _any property in everement change, characteristic, or change_

6. response _An instance of behavior pressing a bar etc_

7. EEG _electroencepalogram_

8. Skinner box _metal box where rat pushes metal bar to get food_

9. habit _Tendency for given stimulus to evoke the same response on successive occasions_

10. comparative psychology _Study of mices + rats to compare them and their reactions to humans_

11. theory _a group of principles from which the occurence of individual events can be logically deduced —_

2

Question:

1. What are the three types of independent variables in psychology?
What empirical laws are derived from each type? Give an example of each.

    a. _____Response_____ R = f (_Stimulus_)

    example: _Reading a book_

    _____

    b. _____Response_____ R = f (_Organism_) ✳

    example: _effects of a sound on somebody_

    c. _____Response_____ R = f (_Respondent_)

    example: _Taking a lie detector test_

2. Why is "common sense" inferior to science?

    a. _Too vague_

    b. _inconsistent_

fails to test   c. _Ignores the need for explanation_

3. Distinguish between <u>factual</u> meaning and <u>operational</u> meaning.
Operational meaning has to do with the definition
of terms and concepts. While factual meaning
has to do with the T or F of scientific statements

✳ 4. What are the attributes of a theoretical construct?

    a. _summize data_

    b. _make prediction about ~~faraday~~ future_

    c. _relate independent and dependent variables_

5. What are the three steps in the scientific method (in order of occurence)?

    a. _Forming a conjecture_

b. _investigation_

c. _interpretation_

Can learning occur during sleep? _No_

How is this known? _Experimentation. The results shoned that nothing was learned while asleep_

Observation

In the study on "sleep learning", what was the dependent variable? independent variable? What type of empirical relationship was studied?

a. Dependent variable _~~Sleep~~ learning_

b. Independent variable _~~Were given answers~~ sleep_

c. R = f (_O_)

7. What does the formula $Y = f(x_1, x_2, x_3, \ldots x_n)$ refer to? _function of a variable on an event_

Y is _a event_

f is _phase or function of_

$x_1, x_2, x_3, \ldots x_n$ are _variable_

8. What is the real difference between various branches of science (i.e., psychology and biology)? _field of study_

9. How may responses be either independent or dependent variables? _some ex_

Objectives

Be able to discuss the major figures mentioned
in this unit with particular reference to Muller,
Helmholz, Fechner, Wundt, Cattell, Ebbinghaus, Watson, Dewey, Pinel, Freud, and Binet.

Describe and relate to the appropriate individual or individuals above the school of psychology
to which they belonged. Note that not all of the
above were associated with a specific school (i.e.
Pinel, Binet) - in this case note their major con-
tributions.

Be able to describe the change from prescien-
tific speculation to the science of psychology.

Be able to describe and differentiate the major
schools of psychology.

Be able to discuss the changing concepts in
deviant behavior from Pinel through Freud.

Be able to discuss the rationale behind intelligence testing and other psychological testing procedures.

Describe the basis of industrial and social
psychology. Understand why it would be appropriate
to describe modern psychology as <u>objective</u>.

Define:

1. British Empiricists   _A group of philosophers who developed
   a reasonable philosophical interpretation of behavior._   P 31

2. Wundt   _- linked with the establishment of psychology (concentrated
   just on the problems of psychology. He established the 1ST psychological laboratory._   P.33

3. Leibzig   _1879   place where the 1ST psychological laboratory
   was established_

4. Muller   _- laid the ground work for an experimental psychology._   P. 32

   STUDENT OF MULLER (CONT. WORK)
5. Helmholtz   _- discovered some of the physical + physiological factors responsible for
   our visual + auditory experiences. His findings were theoretical formulations_   P. 32

6. Fechner   _- use techniques that demonstrated that scientific measurement
   could be used in the study of behavior (methods are used in the investigation of the
   relationships between stimuli + responses._   P. 32

7. introspection   _- method of self-observation that Wundt use
   to investigated conscious experience_   P. 34.

8. Cattell   _said He said that the use of reaction time should be used.
   Using this proved possible to do psychological research with out
   considering the experiences of the st subjects_   P. 35

9. reaction time   _- Time required for a person to respond to a
   stimulus. (eg "light)_   P. 35

10. Ebbinghaus   _memory experiments applied scientific measurement
    to memory process_   P. 35

    he was this
11. nonsense syllable   _a nonsense word consisting of 2 consonants
    and a vowel (eg tav or Xat)_   P 35

12. functionalism   _- an early school of psychology which proposed
    that the function, not the structure, of conscious experience should be
    study. This viewpoint led many Functionalists to investigate behavior
    objectively and thus paved the way for behaviorism._   P. 36

6

13. Watson _____

_____

14. behaviorism *A systematic position, vigorously expounded by John* P. 37-8
B Watson, which maintained that the subject matter was behavior, not
conscious ~~matter~~ experience.

15. Gestalt *a systematic position in psychology which emphasizes principles*
of organization exhibited in behavior and conscious experience P. 38

16. Pinel *- The father of psychiatry (saw that insane were suffering* P. 39
from illness and should be treated ~~as~~ like sick people. Didn't believe it was caused
by supernatural influences.)

17. psychosis *- A severe behavior disorder* P. 41

_____

18. Freud *-* _____

_____

19. psychoanalysis *- methods of personality ~~and~~ analysis and* P. 41
treatment. P. 41 *a method of psychotherapy which attempts to make a person*
aware of his repressed conflicts and motives so that he may
acquire healthier models of responding.

20. unconscious *A concept introduced by Freud to refer to those "mental events"*
which a person is not aware of, even though they influence his behavior. P. 92

21. Binet *- proposed the idea of measuring a child's intelligence.*
(psychological tests). P. 43

22. age-standard method *- method of measuring the intelligence of a child*
in relation to the average performance of different age groups.

23. industrial psychology *- psychologists figures qualifications of people*
for different jobs P. 44.

24. human engineering *- ~~a~~ branch in psychology. (psychologists +*
engineers work together to form machine ~~fo~~ suited to the men who run them

25. social psychology *An area of psychology concerned with*
social influences on individual behavior and group behavior P. 45

26. objective psychology *the contemporary behavioristic point of view that accepts as*
a dependent variable in psychological research any behavior which is publicly
observable or capable of being repeatedly recorded.

7

Questions:

1. Show how the following would differ in their interpretations of the causes of behavior:

a. mystical speculation _- early explanation of human behavior involved the assumption that mystical forces, agents or spirits were responsible_

b. ethical interpretations _interpretations based solely on consistency with a larger philosophical system (not likely to meet requirements of scientific method - consistency with experimental evid_

c. reasonable interpretations _- all knowledge is derived from sense experience, thus emphasizing the role of past experience in determining behavior (common sense)_

d. scientific approach _- must be proved by facts_

2. What is the significance of the date 1879? _The first scientific laboratory for the study of behavior was established (birth date of psychology)._

3. How do introspection, Gestalt psychology and behaviorism differ? _Introspection is describe by self-observation (everyone sees something different) Gestalt psy. emphasizes organization, the quality of wholeness, both in behavior & experience behaviorism is reserch done without any reference to consciousness._

4. Trace the development of the concept of mental illness from demonology to Pinel to Freud. _Thought to be wicked persons possessed by devils so they weren't help by the people but were confined with criminals or in lunatic asylums. Pinel saw they were suffering from an illness and he treated them. Freud went in to the unconscious to find what trouble them (which they didn't know about). Once he found this out he could cure them_

5. Discuss Binet's method. _Was possible to characterize a child's intelligence by objective and quantitative standards and to develop an operational definition of intelligence._

8

6. Characterize the problems which concern industrial psychologists.

To make machines suited for men and to find qualification the people must have in order to fill a certain job.

7. Trace the development of the field of social psychology.

Most psychologists from Wundt on the ~~various~~ recognized social effect psy. Kurt Lewin observed social interaction under controlled experimental situations

8. Why does the author of the text characterize modern psychology as objective psychology?

believe that any behavior publicly observable or capable of being ~~so~~ recorded from repeated observations, can serve as a ~~depent~~ dependent ~~var~~ variable.

Objectives

Be able to define and interrelate the technical terms in this unit. Be able to describe the characteristics of the normal, bimodal, skewed, and rectangular distributions. Be able to define and describe the concept of correlation, including positive, negative, and zero correlations. Be able to distinguish between descriptive and sampling statistics.

Be able to define and distinguish among the following: frequency polygon and histogram; mean, mode, and median; range and standard deviation. Be able to relate "significance", "chance" and the null hypothesis. Be able to state the percentage of scores found within 1, 2, and 3 standard deviations of the mean. Be able to calculate the measures of central tendency, and know what they mean.

Define:

1. descriptive statistics _Arranging and grouping of data to describe a large population of findings in a simple manner._

2. sampling statistics

3. mode _most frequent score_

4. mean _average_

5. median _Middlemost score in distribution_
   _12 5 9 50_

6. standard deviation _dispersion of scores from mean._
   TO GET IT FIRST FIND MEAN THEN SUBTRACT. (EG. 5-SCORES 5,9,10,11,15. MEAN IS 10 DEVIATION IS -5,-1,0,1,5) P.57

7. range _measure of variability between lowest & highest score_ . (TO GET range subtract lowest from highest score).

DIFFERENT SHAPES OF FREQ.

8. normal probability distribution _chance distribution_
   most important

9. rectangular distribution _called R distribution   freq. is the same for all something_

10. bimodal distribution

11. correlation _relationship_

12. random sample _same chance of being rejected. selection_

11

13. frequency polygon

14. histogram

15. null hypothesis _The assumption that the true difference between two statistics (eg. two means), is zero. Sampling statistics are used to reject or retain the null hypothesis._

16. significance _When experiment is not governed by chance_

17. sampling distribution _The distribution of a given statistic calculated from successive samples drawn from the same population (eg. a distribution of means from several samples)_

18. central tendency _Measure of center of distribution_

Questions:

1. Calculate the mean, median, mode and range in the following distribution: 1, 2, 3, 4, 5

    a. mean = _____3_____

    b. median = _____3_____

    c. mode = _____

    d. range = ~~105~~ ~~2~~4

2. What is the possible range of values for the coefficient of correlation? What do they mean? What determines the degree of relationship between variables? _+1.00 To -1.00_____

_____

_____

_____

3. In the normal probability distribution, what percentage of scores fall within

    a. one standard deviation of the mean? _2 & 4_ 68.3% ($\pm$ 1 SD)

    b. two standard deviations of the mean? _1   5_ 95.4% ($\pm$ 2 SD)

    c. three standard deviations of the mean? _0 , 6_ 99.7% ($\pm$ 3 SD)

4. Relate the concepts of significance, chance, and null hypothesis.

_____

_____

_____

_____

Objectives

Be able to lable and describe the major features of the brain. Be able to name and describe the major parts of the central and peripheral nervous systems. Be able to describe the basic neural mechanisms outlined in this unit. Be able to relate central nervous system (CNS) functioning to behavior, and state the role of hormonal systems in affecting behavior.

Understand the basic principles of genetics as they apply to psychology. Be able to relate maturation to behavior.

Define: (include the <u>functions</u> and <u>locations</u> of specific anatomical areas)

1. reflex _____

_____

2. nerve — a bundle of ~~new~~ nerve fibers _____

3. neuron *basic unit of nervous system* FUNCTION: TO TRANSmit NEURAL IMPULSES "it
a single nerve cell consisting of the cell body and ~~nose~~ nerve fibers.

transmit electrical signals capable of generating neural impulses in other neurons.

telodendri

4. dendrites *recicre neural inpulses from other neurons or receptors*
The receiving end of a neuron that is usually stimulated by an external stimulus, receptor activity, or by an neural impulse from a presynaptic axon

myelin sheath
↳ fatty substance around the axon

5. axon *conduct neural impulses*
The fiber of the neuron through which neural impulses are transmitted to the synapse or effector.

6. cell body *~~Perikaryon~~ PERIKARYON is focal point wherein the basic life maintaining functions of the neuron take place.*

7. synapse *point of functional conection between the neurons*

8. acetylcholine *is a chemical transmitter that is emitted when a neural impulses arives at a synapse.*

9. afferent vs. efferent nerves *to (towards) From (carry away) Sensory nerves that connect receptors with the CNS. nerves that connect the CNS with the reacting mechanisms (muscles + glands). sometimes called motor nerves.*

10. all-or-none law ———— *spontaneous act only happens or it does not happen.*

11. absolute and relative refractory phases *unresponsive for* $\frac{1}{1000} - \frac{3}{1000}$ TO STIMULATION sec

$\frac{5}{1000}$

12. autonomic nervous system *controls heart lungs etc mainly responsable for activation of the smooth muscles*

↓ PERIPHERAL NERVOUS SYSTEM *Peripheral n-s*

15

13. genetics _____

_____

14. kinesthesis _Thermastatic action in muscles_

_____

15. frontal lobes _Front_ _____

Parietal Lobe - Upper Back

16. temporal lobes _Bottom_ _____

_____

17. occipital lobes _Rear Portion - Lower_ _____

_____

18. cerebrum _Forebrain - ~~Nerve Tissue~~_ _____

_____

19. cerebellum _Hindbrain - Nerve tissue - Controls_

~~tonicity~~ of sketal muscles -maintains posture and equilibrium

20. corpus callosum _A large tract of fibers that unites the_

two I cerebral hemispheres

21. spinal cord _____

_____

22. thalamus _relay station in fore brain   P. 80_

_____

23. hypothalamus _Controls sleep-walking, cause shivering_

in fore brain

24. pituitary _____

_____

25. reticular activating system _(RAS) a portion of the recticular_

formation that functions to arouse cortical activity.

26. C.N.S. _Central Nervous System_ _____

_____

medulla -controll breathing and Heart beat

27. hormones _The chemical secretions of endocrine (ductless) glands._

28. reciprocal inhibition _P.78._

29. threshold of excitation _amount of energy required to produce stimulation in any nerve fiber_

30. genetics _Science of Heredity_

31. chromosome _contian gene - found in nucleus_

32. DNA _AT C G etc._

33. gene _determines outcome of offspring_

34. maturation _sequence of change in behavior due to physiological growth_

Questions:

1. What are the three primary types of neurons and what are their main functions?

    a. _____ receptors - receiving _____

    _____

    b. _____ Nerve cell - connecting _____

    _____

    c. _____ effector - reacting. _____

    _____

2. What are the two branches of the autonomic nervous system? What are their functions?

    a. _____ Sympathetic - Stress _____

    _____

    b. _____ Parasympathic - Relaxation _____

    _____

    _____

3. Briefly describe the process by which the DNA molecule reproduces itself._____

_____

_____

4. Give examples of how the environment may influence the processes of genetic determination._____

_____

_____

5. How may genetics be related to psychology?_____

_____

_____

7. Label and give the function of the parts of the brain indicated below:

I *forebrain*

a. ~~Cerebral Hemisphere~~ cortex

b. B. ~~Thalamus~~ PITUITARY GLAND

c. ~~Hypothalamus~~
HYPOTHALAMUS

II. *Hindbrain*

midbrain

d. ~~Pons~~ THALAMUS

e. ~~midbrain~~ pons

f. medulla

g. spinal cord

h. Cerebellum

LOBE	FUNCTION
1. FRONTAL	motor
2. Temporal	HEARING
3. Occipital	VISION
4. Parietal	~~Parietal lobe~~

Objectives

Be able to define, explain and relate to one
another the technical terms used in this unit.
Know the three physical properties of light and the
range of the physical stimulus which produces a visual response in man. Be able to describe the various
parts of the eye and the visual system and be able to
discuss the function of each part. Give particular
attention to the retina.

Know what is meant by visibility. Describe the
methods used to find detection thresholds. Be able
to describe and explain the effects of those factors
which influence visibility. Be able to do the same
for visual acuity. Be able to discuss the psychological sensation of brightness and to discuss how varia-
tions in the physical properties of light effect this
sensation. In connection with the effect of wavelength
on brightness, pay particular attention to the relationships among the rods, cones and light intensity and to
how these relationships can produce an effect such as
the Purkinje phenomenon.

Define:

1. wavelength The distance between crests of successive waves

2. visible spectrum - when white light is separated.

3. white light - a light that is composed of many different colors

4. spectrally homogeneous light - a light of a single color.

5. composition The assortment of wavelengths composing a beam of light.

6. intensity - energy level

7. retina light sensitive surface.

8. fovea - it is an indented, small area in the center of the retina, where the cones are tightly packed

9. rods - receptors in the shape of rods that are sensitive to light Vision is mediated solely by rods in moonlight or starlight

10. cones - vision is mediated by cones when the light is more intense.

11. blind spot - found slightly below the fovea and in toward the nose There are no receptors here all individual nerve fibers from the retina converge here to form optic nerve

12. optic nerve - where nerve fibers from the retina converge. The blind spot.

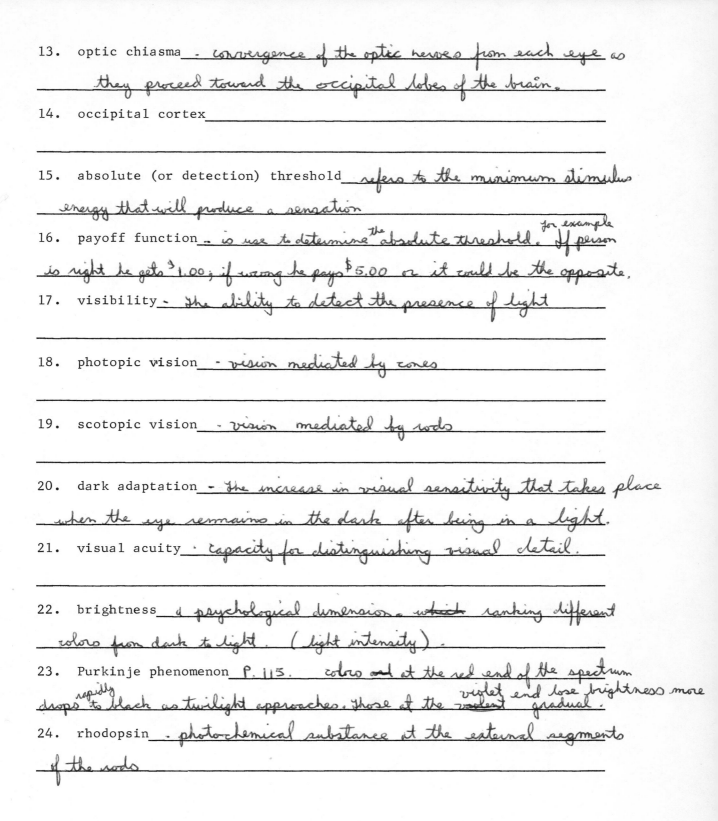

13. optic chiasma - convergence of the optic nerves from each eye as they proceed toward the occipital lobes of the brain.

14. occipital cortex

15. absolute (or detection) threshold refers to the minimum stimulus energy that will produce a sensation

16. payoff function - is use to determine the absolute threshold. for example If person is right he gets $1.00; if wrong he pays $5.00 or it could be the opposite.

17. visibility - the ability to detect the presence of light

18. photopic vision - vision mediated by cones

19. scotopic vision - vision mediated by rods

20. dark adaptation - the increase in visual sensitivity that takes place when the eye remains in the dark after being in a light.

21. visual acuity · capacity for distinguishing visual detail.

22. brightness a psychological dimension - which ranking different colors from dark to light. (light intensity).

23. Purkinje phenomenon P. 115. colors and at the red end of the spectrum drops rapidly to black as twilight approaches. those at the violet end lose brightness more gradual.

24. rhodopsin · photochemical substance at the external segments of the rods

Questions:

1. What are the three physical properties of light?

   a. *wavelengths*

   b. *composition*

   c. *intensity*

2. What is the range of the visible spectrum (in nanometers)? _____
   400 and 800 nm

3. Where are the cones most densely concentrated? *fovea, center of the retina*

4. Where are the rods concentrated? *20° from the fovea*

5. How does one measure the absolute (detection) threshold? _____

6. What receptors mediate (are responsible for) scoptopic vision? *rods*
   _____ photopic vision? *cones*

7. What factors influence acuity?

   a. *Retina (cones and rods) Angle of retinal stimulation*

   b. *wavelength. Light intensity*

   c. *Dark adaptation Brightness*

8. What factors influence visibility?

   a. *Retina (cones and rods)*

   b. *wavelength*

   c. *Dark adaptation*

9. Distinguish between visibility and visual acuity. _____
   visibility is the ability to sense light and acuity is the ability to distinguish fine detail

10. What relationship does rhodopsin have to dark adaptation? _____

rhodopsin is regenerated in the dark dark. _____

_____

_____

11. How are brightness and intensity related? _____

_____

_____

_____

12. What effect does wavelength have upon brightness? _____

different wave lengths with the same intensity will make

the brightness different. _____

_____

13. List the characteristics that differentiate rods and cones.

        Rods   Cones

a._____   _receptors for color vision_

b._____   _____

c._____   _____

d._____   _____

e._____   _____

14. What characteristics of rods and cones account for the Purkinje

phenomenon? _When it gets dark the rods function and the cones do not_

causing this effect. _____

_____

_____

Objectives

Be able to relate the three psychological dimensions of color to the three physical dimensions of light.
Understand how the color solid shows the relationships
among these three psychological dimensions, and how it
shows the effects of color mixture. In this latter
connection, pay close attention to complementary hues
and to the distinction between additive and subtractive
color mixture.

Be able to describe and explain color blindness
and color weakness, and be able to describe the com-
pensations a color blind person can make. Be able to
state and explain the duplexity theory of vision and
to list the facts which support this theory. Know the
major aspects of the two theories of color vision, how
they differ and what evidence there is for or against
each.

Be able to describe the electrical activity of the
nerve cells of the visual system and to relate this
activity to phenomena such as light adaptation, brightness perception, and stabilized retinal images.

Define:

1. hue _- gives a color its name   Characteristic or dimension of_
visual sensation that results from stimulation by lights of different wavelength

2. brightness _- light to dark_

3. saturation _- refers to the amount of hue a color has._ SEE Page 115

4. color solid _- Where all 3 dimensions of color sensitivity can be_
represented simultaneously in the shape of a double cone

WHITE
HUE
BLACK
P. 116

5. additive color mixture

6. subtractive color mixture

7. complementary colors _- two hues that are opposite of each other or_
which when mixed together will produce gray.

8. white light

9. color blindness _- ~~people who can not see~~_ a visual defect _that prevents a person_
~~for~~ from detecting differences in hue.

10. red-green color blindness _- people can't see red + green but only as poorly_
saturated _yellows or browns . (the most commmone)_

11. nystagmus _- a behavior that indicates that a totally color-blind_
person is blind in this area

12. duplexity theory of vision _-_

13. Young-Helmholtz theory of color vision *a theory that says that there are three types of cones and they respond differently to various light waves,*

14. Hering theory of color vision *is like the one below except there are three opponent pairs of visual systems*

15. light adaptation *- light of a contant physical intensity will become less bright when staring at it for a while.*

16. "on" fibers (or cells) *- transmit impulses only when light is on.*

17. "off" fibers

18. "on-off" fibers

Questions:

1. Fill in the table below

    Physical property of light Psychological sensation or response

    a._____ a._____

    b._____ b._____

    c._____ c._____

2. What are the complementary colors for the following?

    a. blue _yellow_

    b. red _blue - green_

    c. green_____

    d. yellow _blue_

    e. What does the mixture of complementary colors produce? _gray_

    _____

3. How do additive and subtractive color mixtures differ?_____

    subtractive is when pigment mixture colors eliminate each other

    _____

    _____

4. The duplexity theory states:

    a. _There are two kinds of visual receptors - rods and cones_

    _____

    b. _Rods and cones are distributed differently over the_
    retina.

    c. _Rods operate at low intensities of light and imitate colorless sensations_
    of various degrees of brightness; cones react at higher intensities
    and instigate sensations of colors

5. What is some of the evidence for the duplexity theory?

    a._____

    b._____

c. _____

d. _____

e. _____

f. _____

6. The Young-Helmholtz theory holds that there are three different kinds of receptors for color.

    a. What colors do they respond to? _red, blue, and green_

    b. What produces the sensation of white? _equal portion of all three_

    c. What color provides the most trouble for this theory? _____

yellow because there a part of the retina sensitive to yellow but not to red and green

7. What are the opponent pairs in the Hering theory?

    a. _yellow - blue_

    b. _red - green_

    c. _white - black_

8. What is the relationship between brightness and the rate of neural impluses in the optic nerve? _____

_____

_____

9. What is the effect of stabilizing an image on the retina? _____

_____

Why does this occur? _____

_____

10. How do the three types of fibers in the retina respond to the on-set and offset of a light?

    a. "on" fibers _respond only when light is one_

    b. "off" fibers _"   "   " the " is turned off or on_

    c. "on-off" fibers _" " " " " " turned off or on_

Objectives

Know the three physical properties of sound, the measurement of these properties, the ranges within which sounds can be heard, and the relationships of the physical properties to the three psychological dimensions of audition. Be able to describe and explain the functions of the various parts of the ear and the auditory nervous system.

Be able to state and explain the four theories of hearing and the volley principle. Be able to indicate the relationships among these theories. Know the evidence for and against each theory.

Know the four basic taste sensations and the relationship between taste and smell. Be able to describe the changes in sensory capacity produced by adaptation and by age.

Define:

1. frequency _- measured in cycles per second (cps)_

2. intensity _- amount of pressure_

3. complexity _- a wave that has many tone. When one is complex, it repeats itself._

4. pitch _- psychological characteristic of sound waves. (function of frequency)_ _not exclusively_ _judging which two tones is high higher, you are discriminating between their pitch_

5. loudness _- some what dependent on frequency)_

6. timbre _- depends upon the composition of sound waves_ _so a note would sound different on a piano and a violin even if the same loudness. you can tell because of the timbre_

7. white noise _- a hissing sound that contains all frequencies in the same way that a white light contains all frequencies of the visible spectrum._

8. ossicles _- three small bones where vibrations are transmitted (in ear)_

9. tympanic membrane _- ear drum (tightly stretched membrane at the auditory canal inner end.   (in ear)_

10. frequency theory _a theory of hearing which assumes that the sensation of pitch is a function of the frequency of neural impulses transmitted through the auditory nerve._

11. volley principle _The nerve fibers within the auditory nerve operate in squads_

12. place-frequency theory _a theory of hearing which assumes that the sensation of pitch is due both to the portion of the basilar membrane stimulated and the frequency of neural impulses in the auditory nerve._

13. adaptation _refers to the change in sensitivity that results from important sen stimulation or the lack of it._

Questions:

1. Fill in the table

    Physical property of sound   Psychological sensation

    a._____   _____

    b._____   _____

    c._____   _____

2. What evidence disproved Helmholtz's theory?_____

_____

3. What physiological fact argues against the frequency theory? In
what way did the volley principle help the frequency theory explain this

_____

_____

_____

4. How does the Place-frequency theory explain the sensation of low
tones (under 1000 cps)?_____

_____

    high tones?_____

_____

5. List the four basic taste sensations

    a. _sweet_____   c. _salt_____

    b. _sour_____   d. _bitter_____

6. What other sense accounts for what most people call "taste"?

_smell_____

7. How does the taste sensitivity of the new born child compare with
that of the adult? _It is lower than the adult._____

8. How rapidly do these senses adapt:

    smell:_____

    taste:_____   hearing:_____

Objectives

Be able to define perception and distinguish
it from sensation. Be able to define and discuss
the figure-ground relationship. Know the three
laws of perceptual grouping and be able to give
examples of each.

Be able to list, describe, and explain all
the cues to visual depth perception. Be able to
explain the operation of the auditory space perception. Include both the stimulus cues, the three
organismic cues, and the use of auditory cues by
the blind.

Define:

1. perception _relates behavior to complex patterns of stimuli_

_____

2. figure-ground _- a figure that stands out from the background falls into this group._

3. perceptual grouping _the tendency to perceive discrete stimuli in an organized manner._

4. principle of nearness _- Stimulus elements that are close together tend to be perceived as belonging together._

5. principle of similarity _The greater the similarity among stimuli the more likely they will be perceived as part of common group._

6. principle of continuity _Stimulus elements that are part of a continuous sequence tend to be grouped together (eg ( ) ; we fill in the gap)._

7. visual depth perception _- see things in a three dimensional way_

_____

8. relative size _- can create distance by varying the size of objects (eg make one man smaller than other would mean he is in the background)._

9. linear perspective _- The arrangement of lines in a drawing to produce a representation of depth. (eg railroad tracks converging)._

10. interposition _- When two objects are in the same line of vision, the nearer one conceals at least part of the farther one._

11. light and shadow _The appropriate distribution of lights and shadows can give a the two dimensional drawing a three dimensional look_

12. clearness _- The nearer to an object, the clearer it is._

_____

13. movements (motion parallax) The speed of an object as it travels through space can serve as a cue to its distance.

14. adjacency is when two objects are next two each other but are made to look like one is behind the other.

15. gradients spacing of horizontal lines come get closer as distance increase.

16. accomodation - The change in lens shape (retina) lens bulges when we look at a nearby object.

17. convergence far object vision is parallel - closer they converge.

18. retinal disparity The reception of different images by each eye

19. binaural cues - the use of two ears

20. median plane - a place where sound hits both ears at the same time.

21. pseudophone - A device that makes ^a person locate a sound as coming from the ^side opposite to its origin.

Questions:

1. List and explain the STIMULUS cues for visual depth perception.

   a. _Relative size_

   b. _Linear perspective_

   c. _Interposition_

   d. _Light and shadow_

   e. _clearness._

   f. _movements_

   g. _gradients_

   h. _adjacency_

2. List and explain the ORGANISMIC cues for visual depth perception.
   Which is the most important?

   a. _accommodation_

   b. _convergence_

   c. _retinal disparity - most important_

3. How do blind persons locate obstacles? _by sound and feel._

4. What are the stimulus cues for auditory space perception?

   a. _intensity (sound decreases with distance)_

   b. _timbre (at distance will sound the same._

5. What are three different BINAURAL cues that allow a person to locate
   a sound?

   a. _it either reaches one of your ears before the other_ (the one closer to where the sound is coming from

   P. 158 b. _is stronger on the other the other side_

   c. _is different in phase_

   d. Do these cues allow one to locate a sound from the medial plane?

   _no_ Explain. _reaches both ears at same time_

e. What does the pseudophone do to these cues? _makes them_

opposite .

Objectives

Be able to describe the different constancies
and tell how they change with age. Be able to relate the phenomena that account for Mach Bands, the
horizontal-vertical illusion, and the moon illusion.
Be able to describe the effect of value on size perception. Be able to tell what variables influence
attention.

Define:

1. size constancy _The resistance of a visually perceived object to change in size as its retinal image changes in size_

2. shape constancy _The shape of a familiar object remains stable in spite of the fact that the retinal image it varies widely_

3. brightness constancy _- when brightness stays the same in day or night_

4. albedo _- the percentage of reflect will be the same no matter what the available light is ._

5. color constancy _____

6. Mach bands _a visual phenomenon that occurs at the boundary between two areas of markedly different intensities in which an observer perceives a narrow bright band on the lighter side of the border & a narrow darker band on the other side_

7. neural inhibition _____

8. horizontal-vertical illusion _The vertical line looks longer_

9. apparent movement _- when there is no movement, but appears to be moving_

10. phi phenomenon _- name of apparent movement_

11. moon illusion _- deals with the moon, near horizon the moon appears much larger than it does in the sky._

12. attention _selectivity of the perceptual processes_

13. perceptual satiation The tendency for a perception to weaken after prolonged exposure.

14. intensity Stimulus that stands out intensely (eg. trade name on billboard are pub printed in large, bright letters).

15. contrast Stimulus that stand out in contrast with the background get attention.

16. movement movement attracts and maintains attention.

17. perceptual set The tendency of an organism to pay attention to certain features of a stimulus pattern.

18. visual cliff - a device that makes a visual cliff.

19. temporal lobes

Questions:

1. What is the relationship between albedo and brightness constancy?

_____

_____

_____

2. a. How does the size constancy of children and adults differ? What is the effect of observational distance? For shot short distances (10 feet) both exhibited perfect size constancy. With increasing distances children showed less and less constancy

    b. How do the other constancies change with age? they improve

3. What produces Mach bands? result from the mechanism of retinal inhibition

4. What is the effect of the shape of the visual field on the H-V illusion? When the shape is longer in length than width the V line will look longer but if it is the opposite the H line will look longer.

5. a. What is the effect of value on the perception of size of coins and poker chips? _____

    _____

    b. Describe the study done with "rich" and "poor" subjects. _____

    _____

    _____

6. List the three stimulus variable that influence attention.
    a. Intensity _____
    b. Contrast _____
    c. movement _____

7. What were the resluts of the "visual cliff" experiments?_____

___~~mas~~ most of them stay on the shallow side and did not
venure over the cliff _____

_____

8. What were the results of the experiment on the physiology of attention by Hernandez-Peon?_____

_____

_____

9. What were the results of Penfield's experiment?_____

_____

_____

_____

Objectives

Be able to describe the basic process of classical conditioning and give examples of classically
conditioned responses in humans and lower animals.
Discuss the stages and basic phenomena of classical
conditioning, with emphasis on aquisition, extinction, spontaneous recovery, stimulus generalization
and discrimination. Be able to differentiate between positive, negative and secondary reinforcement.
Relate secondary reinforcement to higher-order conditioning.

Define:

1. learning _is a change in behavior resulting from practice_
_____

2. conditioning _simplest form of learning, deals with the formation,_
strengthening and weakening of S-R associations resulting from practice .

3. classical or respondent conditioning _experimental method used_
by Pavlov - A conditioned stimulus is paired with a unconditioned stimulus

4. unconditioned stimulus (US) _the stimulus that elicits the unconditioned_
response

5. unconditioned response (UR) _the responce that is made to the_
unconditioned stimulus

6. conditioned stimulus (CS) _paired with unconditioned stimulus_
acquires capacity to evoke response similar to the one unconditioned stimulus made

7. conditioned response (CR) _response evoked by conditioned stimulus_
after conditioning has taken place

8. acquisition stage _time when patient learns new association_
between condition stimulus and conditioned response

9. amplitude of response _The amount of response_
_____

10. latency of response _time interval between the on set of_
stimulus and the occurence of the response

11. response produced cues _when an organisum generate his own_
stimulus to serve as a cue cue for his own behavior

12. extinction _when a condition response is weaken or_
gradually eliminated.

45

13. reinforcement _an event that increases the tendency for a stimulus to evoke a response_

14. positive reinforcer _reinforcement which strengthens an association between stimulus and response by its presentation_

15. negative reinforcer _reinforcement which strengthen an association between stimulus and response by termination._

16. spontaneous recovery _reappearence of extinguished conditioned response after time interval in which no practice occured_

17. stimulus generalization _tendency for stimuli similar to conditioned stimulus to evoke a conditioned response_

18. conditioned discrimination _combining of acquisition and extinction procedure for training organism to response to a conditioned stimulus and not generalized one_

19. higher-order conditioning _when a previously conditioned stimulus functions as an unconditioned stimulus to establish a new conditioned response_

20. secondary reinforcer _a previously neutral stimulus that acquires reinforcing properties._

Questions:

1. What are the three essential features of classical or respondent conditioning?

   a. _An unconditioned stimulus that evokes an unconditioned response_

   b. _a to-be-conditioned stimulus that does not initially evoke the unconditioned response_

   c. _Paired presentations of the conditioned and unconditioned stimuli_

2. How does the LATENCY and AMPLITUDE of a conditioned response change in each of the following stages?

   a. acquisition: latency _of conditioned response is decreasing_
   amplitude _increases_

   b. extinction: latency _increased_
   amplitude _decreased_

   c. spontaneous recovery: latency _decreased_
   amplitude _increased_

3. What were the US, CS, UR, and CR in each of the following studies described in your text?

   a. eyelid conditioning _CS is a weak light   CR - the 3rd record or the 3rd trial._ _UR - the reflex closing of the lid   US - a puff of air_

   b. urinary conditioning _UR the patients expression of an urge to urinate   US the pressure in the bladder   CS dials place in front of patients   CR wanted to urinate when little in bladder._

   c. vasoconstriction _US - shock and ice water   CS - buzzer_

4. Describe the relationship between stimulus generalization and the ease of establishing a conditioned discrimination. _____

_____

_____

47

5. How are the concepts of secondary reinforcement and higher-order conditioning related?_____

_____

_____

6. Assume that fear is a conditioned response which was established by presenting a neutral stimulus (CS) with a painful one (US). Describe how a child could show a fear response (CR) to a dog (CS) by the following procedures:

    a. first-order conditioning:_____

    _____

    _____

    b. second-order conditioning:_____

    _____

    _____

48

Objectives

Describe the basic phenomena of instrumental (operant) conditioning. Be able to describe and graph the different reinforcement schedules--pay particular attention to the characteristic behavior peculiar to each

Be able to discuss the effects of intermittent reinforcement with regard to resistance to extinction. Be able to discuss discrimination learning, generalization gradients, and the Guttman and Kalish study.

Note: In this WORKBOOK we will make no distinction between the terms "instrumental conditioning" and "operant conditioning".

Define:

1. instrumental (or operant) conditioning _the organism changes its environment_

2. primary reinforcer _a reinforcer such as food or water, that reduces a homeostatic drive_

3. conditioned (or secondary) reinforcer _Stimuli that acquire ~~their own reinforcing properties~~ reinforcing properties_

4. generalized conditioned reinforcer _Stimuli that acquire their own reinforcing properties after preceding a large number of primary reinforcer_

5. escape conditioning _when a stimuli learn to escape something by pressing something, ~~eg~~ like a bar_

6. avoidance conditioning _— when a stimuli learns to press a bar in order to avoid pain_

7. extinction _~~nonreinforcement trials~~_

8. stimulus generalization _The tendency for stimuli similar to the stimulus to evoke a condition response_

9. response rate _The measure of behavior used in operant conditioning   response rate = $\frac{\text{\# of responses}}{\text{unit of time}}$_

10. cumulative record (or cumulative response curve) _when bar is pressed a pen moves upward, raising the line a notch._

11. operant level _The rate of emitting an instrumental response prior to any reinforced training_

12. schedule of reinforcement _a program of successive reinforcements and nonreinforcements_

13. continous reinforcement (or CRF) an animal is reinforced consistently every time he makes the appropriate response

14. intermittent reinforcement - when a group recieves reinforcement randomly

15. fixed ratio (FR) a specified number of responses have to occur before reinforcement is given

16. variable ratio (VR) reinforcement occur after varying numbers of responses

17. fixed interval (FI) reinforcement are given after a predetermined time interval

18. variable interval (VI) reinforced after intervals which vary in time

19. scalloping the rate of response is low for the period immediately following reinforcement but rises as the time for next reonforcement approches
Found in a fixed interval schedule

20. resistance to extinction an intermittent reinforcement schedule produces the greater resistance to extinction p. 207 figure 7.22

21. S^D stimulus present during reinforcement

22. S^Δ ''   ''   '' nonreinforcement

23. discrimination when a subject learns to responsed to a conditioned stimulus and not to a generalized stimulus

24. generalization gradient - a graph

Questions:

1. Describe the basic procedure for establishing a conditioned instrumental (operant) response, including the measurement of the response in each stage of conditioning._____

_____

_____

2. Relate escape conditioning to negative reinforcement._____

_____

_____

_____

3. Distinguish between escape and avoidance conditioning._____

_____

_____

_____

4. An experimenter wishes to train a pigeon to peck at a key illuminated by a green light but not a red one.

    a. Which key would produce a reinforcer if pecked?___green_____

    b. What would be the term for that key? S^D_____

    c. Which key would not be reinforced?_____red_____

    d. What is the term for that key?_____S^Δ_____

    e. What would happen to the rates of responding on each key during:

        i. Operant level

           a. Red___~~one~~ decrease____

           b. Green___increase_____

        ii. Acquisition

           a. Red___decrease____

           b. Green___increase____

f. What is this type of learning called?_____

5. What is the most important effect of intermittent reinforcement?___

That during extinction subjects make more responses over a longer period of time.

_____

6. Describe the study by Guttman and Kalish (1956). What did the study demonstrate about generalization gradients?_____

Indicated that the strength of the response to the generalized stimulus depends on its similarity to the stimulus that was originally conditioned.

_____

_____

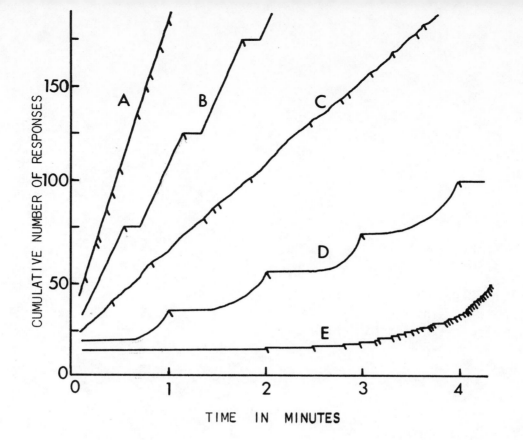

TIME IN MINUTES

7. Identify the schedules in the cumulative record above:

A. _____

B. _____

C. _____

D. _FIXED_ _INTERVAL_ _____

E. _CONTINUOUS_ _REINFORCEMENT_ (crf)

8. Which curve above shows:

a. _____ The highest overall rate of responding.

b. _____ The lowest overall rate of responding.

c. _____ The steadiest rate of responding.

9. How many responses are required for reinforcement in the FR schedule?

_____.

10. What is the interval in the FI schedule?_____

11. How long did the subject on the continuous reinforcement schedule(crf) take to make his _first_ response? __2__ minute(s). Approximately how many responses did he make in the first three minutes?_14_____How many reinforcements did he obtain in the first three minutes? __4____

12. Which subject would show the least resistance to extinction?_____

Which schedules would produce the most resistance to extinction?_____

54

Objectives

Describe the various factors that influence
conditioning. Distinguish between instrumental
and classical conditioning, and learning and
performance, and be able to explain the relationship between responding, habit, drive and inhibition. Be able to relate the studies in this
unit to the phenomena of stimulus generalization
and the reinforcing effects of electrical brain
stimulation.

Define:

1. backward conditioning *The presentation of the unconditioned stimulus prior to the conditioned*

2. intertrial interval *The time interval between successive trials in a learning experiment.*

3. learning

4. performance *- the way an animal acts*

5. habit (H) *The tendency of a stimulus situation to evoke a response. (determines what is done)*

6. drive (D) *determines whether it is done. energizing mechanism that activates a habit.*

7. inhibition(I) *A theoretical construct that refers to the negative or retarding effect certain variables have upon conditioning*

8. RNA *ribonucleic acid*

9. generalization gradient

10. non-differential training

11. differential training *reinforce only when tone is on not off*

12. monochromatic light

56

Questions:

1. Tell how each of these influence conditioning:

    a. amount of reinforced practice_____

    _____

    b. amount of non-reinforced practice_____

    _____

    c. CS - US interval_____

    _____

    d. amount of reinforcement_____

    _____

    e. quality of reinforcement_____

    _____

    f. delay of reinforcement_____

    _____

    g. effort_____

    _____

    h. massing of trials_____

    _____

2. Distinguish between classical (respondent) and instrumental (operant)
conditioning._____

_____

_____

3. Distinguish between learning (H) and performance (R)._____

_____

_____

_____

4. What is the theoretical formula relating R, H, D, and I?_____

$$R = f(H \times D) - I$$

5. What happens to performance (R) in each of the following cases?

   a. H is low_____   d. H is high_____

   b. D is low_____   e. D is high_____

   c. I is low_____   f. I is high_____

6. What do the following studies indicate concerning the development of stimulus generalization?

   a. Jenkins and Harrison (1960) _That stimulus generalization does not get ~~lower~~ lower response when they move from the organial stimulus_____

   b. Peterson (1962) _that the subject did not respond any differently to the organial stimulus than the generaliza stimulus_____

7. How are the reinforcing effects of electrical stimulation of the brain similar to and different from the effects obtained with other reinforcers?

   a. similar_____

   _____

   b. different_____

   _____

Objectives

Be able to relate the concepts of homeostasis,
specific hungers, and balanced diet with each other
and with the concepts of drive, incentive, and organic needs. Be able to discuss the role of the
hypothalamus in controlling consummatory and other
types of instrumental responses.

Be able to discuss the relative importance of
sex hormones and the cerebral cortex in determining
sexual behavior in higher as opposed to lower animals,
and male as opposed to female organisms.

Be able to define "instinct" and make a clear
distinction between drives associated with instincts
and instrumental responses which reduce or eliminate
those drives. Be able to relate positive and negative reinforcers to appetitive and aversive drives.

Define:

✻ 1. drive *A condition or state of the organism which activates and directs his behavior*

2. drive stimulus *The cue resulting from a drive*

3. incentive *A commodity or condition capable of reducing or eliminating a drive; a goal. (or goal)*

4. instrumental (operant) response *A response that acts upon the environment (eg, the bar-pressing behavior of the rat, the disk pecking response of the pigeon)*

5. consummatory response

✻ 6. homeostasis *The tendency of an organism to maintain a condition of physiological equilibrium.*

7. specific hungers *when you want a certain kind of food.*

hunger 8. (approach) appetitive drives *A drive having incentives requiring approach and consummatory responses (eg. hunger → food → eating).*

pain 9. (avoidence) aversive drives *A drive that is reduced by escape from noxious stimulation*

10. hyperphagia *The consumption of abnormal amounts of food. This condition can be produced by lesions in certain areas of the hypothalamus.*

11. aphagia *inability to swallow*

12. hypothalamus *A structure located below the thalamus, containing centers that influence many physiological drives, such as hunger & thirst.*

DRIVE - instrumental response - incentive - drive reduction

60

13. estrogen _ovarian hormones_____

_____

14. instinct_____

_____

15. imprinting _very rapid learning that occurs in some animals during a critical early stage in their development. It is believed by some investigators to lay the basis for ~~fusture~~ future social development._

Questions:

1. Describe the relationship between organic needs and drives. *When our physiological condition has diverged to some extent from this optimal balance, an organic is said to exist*

    a. Do all organic needs result in drives? *No*

    b. Do all drives result from organic needs? *No*

    c. Give examples of both cases. *Suffocation resulting from inhaling excessive amounts of carbon monoxide CO_2 is a tragic example of an organic need that does not produce a drive*

2. What effects do the following have on the sexual behavior of lower as opposed to higher organisms?

    a. Hormones *The higher up on the evolutionary scale you go the more signs you find that signs you find that sexual behavior has become emancipated from hormonal control.*

    b. Cerebral cortex *plays a larger part in the sexual behavior of animals higher in the evolutionary scale.*

3. Differentiate between appetitive (approach) and aversive (avoidance) drives. How are they EMPIRICALLY and OPERATIONALLY defined? How do EACH relate to the positive and negative reinforcers?

4. How are drives and incentives important in learning? (see above)

5. What are the two functions of drive states?

a. _activating behavior (hunger activates the bar-pressing of rats)_

b. _exert a steering function on behavior_

6. What are the four stages of the human sexual response?

a. _the excitement phase_

b. _the plateau phase_

c. _the orgasmic phase_

d. _the resolution phase_

✳ 7. What are the four criteria for instinctive behavior?

a. _The behavior is complex_

b. _is rather rigidly patterned_

c. _is not learned_

d. _is found in all members of the species._

63

Objectives

Be able to discuss intrinsically motivated
behavior and learned drives, and give examples.
Be able to discuss the experiments by Harlow,
Miller, and Schacter and Singer. Be able to
describe the variables that affect manipulation, visual exploration, curiosity, contact-
comfort, and hunger.

Define:

1. learned drive _A drive acquired through learning_

★ 2. intrinsically motivated behavior _Instrumental responses that are self - reinforcing_ (3 of them) _curiosity, manipulation, contact & comfort._

3. placebo and epinephrine _→ a drug which affects the sympathetic system_

★ 4. achievement motive _The drive to perform well in a given task, in short, to be successfull_

5. curiosity

6. fear

7. emotion (as defined by James) _is a sensation of bodily changes_

8. emotion (as defined by Schacter and Singer) _physiological arousal and the person's interpretation of the situation._

Questions:

1. Which of the following are positive reinforcers? Negative reinforcers? What situations demonstrate this?

    a. Brain stimulation_____

_____

    b. Fear reduction_____

_____

    c. Visual exploration_____

_____

    d. Contact comfort_____

_____

    e. Food___+_____

_____

    f. Pain_____

_____

    g. Attention_____

_____

2. What is the effect of the following independent variables upon the associated dependent variables?

    a. age on: manipulation$^{\times}$_____

_____

    b. epinephrine on: emotion_____

_____

    c. deprivation of visual stimuli on: visual exploration_____

_____

    d. complexity of visual stimuli on: visual exploration_____

_____

3. Describe Harlow's experiments with:

a. Manipulation_____

_____

_____

b. Cloth and wire mothers_____

_____

_____

4. Describe Miller's experiment on fear as a learned drive. What kind of conditioning was involved?_____

_____

_____

_____

5. What do learned drives and conditioned reinforcers have in common?

_____

_____

_____

_____

6. Describe Schacter and Singer's experiment. What did it demonstrate? What were the independent and dependent variables?_____

_____

_____

_____

_____

Objectives

Note: This unit utilizes many of the terms developed in Units 11 and 12. Before completing this study guide, it is suggested that you review those definitions.

Be able to define and interrelate the technical terms and phenomena outlined in this unit. Be able to discuss the effects of habit on <u>reversal learning.</u> Be able to discuss the processes and procedures of chaining, shaping and superstitious behavior. Be able to describe the permanance of the effects of: 1. contingent and non-contingent punishment; 2. mild and severe punishment; 3. punishment when an alternate response is available.

Define:

1. habit competition _The tendency for a stimulus to evoke incompatible habits_

2. habit chaining _The integration of successive S-R associations to form a behavior sequence_

3. response-produced cues _A cue that results from an organism's response and which in turn becomes associated with subsequent behavior_

4. selective learning _- When an organism has to select one of 2 possible responses_

5. reversal learning _____

6. reinforcement _-_ _____

7. motivation _____

8. punishment _- application of noxious stimulation_

9. suppression _The elimination of a response for a period of time._

10. contingent punishment _- punishment given to an organism on a response_

11. non-contingent punishment _- punishment given to an organism when ever felt like giving him one_ P. 288

12. alternative responses _- responses that a rat must make to get food. a different path then the one that he learned to take_

69

13. chaining - segments of behavior that are chained together to produce smooth - flowing behavior

14. shaping - technique by which the behavior of an organism is molded

15. response generalization - when responses are repeated, they were differ

16. successive approximations helping a pigeon peck a dish P. 294

17. discriminitive stimulus - a stimulus that has a dual function of evoking and maintaining behavior

18. superstitious behavior - learning to do something because it feels lucking - P. 298

19. non-contingent reinforcement reinforcement occur no matter what organism is doing

20. differential reinforcement The procedure used in operant conditioning to establish a discrimination between two stimuli.

Questions:

1. What effect would high drive have on the following stages of reversal learning?

    a. early in reversal_____

_____

    b. late in reversal_____

_____

2. What are the usual effects of mild punishment of an operant response as compared with severe punishment? What are some possible undesirable side-effects of punishment? What are the effects of delay of punishment? Under what conditions is punishment most effective?

    a. Weak punishment_____

_____

    b. Strong punishment_____

_____

    c. Side effects_____

_____

    d. Effects of delay_____

_____

    e. Most effective_____

_____

3. What type of reinforcement results in "superstitious" behavior? What types of situations produce "superstitious" behavior in humans? Give an example._____

_____

_____

_____

71

4. A child breaks a window and later tells his mother. At that point, the mother punishes him. What response is really being punished?_____

_____

_____

5. How is chaining established? What kind of cues mediate chaining? Give an example of chaining in human behavior._____

_____

_____

_____

_____

6. How is shaping accomplished?_____

_____

_____

_____

7. What three concepts are important in shaping?

   a. _response generalization_____

   _____

   b. _successful habit competition_____

   _____

   c. _each segoment of in the chain must be link togther_

   _____

8. How could you tell if a stimulus was a punisher or reinforcer for a non-verbal organism (e.g. a dog)?_____

_____

_____

_____

Objectives

Be able to relate the phenomena in the area
of sensorimotor learning (such as reminiscence,
warm-up, and knowledge of results) to the phenomena
in operant (instrumental) conditioning such as
spontaneous recovery and reinforcement.

Understand the relationship between massed
practice and work inhibition, and be able to
describe the conditions which produce the most
efficient learning.

Be sure to be able to define and/or give examples of all the terms in this unit.

V

Define:

1. verbal learning _learning that involves language_
   motor " .

2. sensorimotor skill _used in place of the simpler motor skill ·_
   involves both verbal + motor learning

3. spaced practice _learning with rest inbetween_

4. massed practice _– continuous learning_

5. work inhibition _A negitive process that operates to inhibit_
   the performance of a motor skill

6. reminiscence _A sudden improvement in p performance_
   following a rest interval with no practice

7. warm-up _Rapid improvement in performance during a practice_
   period immediately after a long rest period.

8. paired-associate learning _The learning of pairs of syllables, digits, or words_
   so the first member of the pair, the stimulus term, evokes the 2nd member of the
   pair, the response term

9. serial learning _The learning of a series of syllables, digits, or words in_
   a predetermined order.

10. knowledge of results

11. nonsense syllables

12. backward association _An association in which a response term_
    evokes a stimulus term which immediately preceded it.
    A-B to B-A

    conditioning is a form of motor learning

74

13. remote associations _An association in serial learning formed between items that are not adjacent (eg. between the 2ND and 4TH items in a list of nonsense syllables_

14. intrusion errors _An inappropriately placed response in serial learning (eg. responding with the 4TH item in place of the 3RD item)_

15. anticipatory errors _An error in serial learning in which the subject makes a response before it appropriate (eg he responds to the 5TH item with the 7TH item_

16. perseveratory errors _A response in serial learning which would have been correct earlier (eg responding to the 5TH item with the 2ND item)_

17. probability learning _A kind of learning experiment in which the subject must choose which of two events well occur._

18. positive transfer _The facilitating effect prior learning has on present learning or performance._

19. negative transfer _The interfering effect of prior learning on present learning or performance_

20. mediated transfer _The an organism learns to make a new response to an old stimulus with relative ease because he has previously learned an intermediate response which functions as a cue to mediate transfers from the 1st to the 2ND._

21. transposition _____

22. bilateral transfer _transfer of ~~one~~ skill from one limb to its opposite member_

23. learning sets _A case of positive transfer in which an organism increases his speed of learning successive problems of the same general type. He learns how to learn._

24. corpus callosum _A large ~~tact~~ tract of fibers that unites the two ~~coue~~ cerebral hemisphere._

cross education — the positive transfer of a skill acquired by one part of the body to another part.

Questions:

1. What are the effects of massed vs. spaced (distributed) practice on learning? How is "work inhibition" related to these effects?_____

_____

_____

_____

2. How is reminiscence similar to spontaneous recovery? How is it different?_____

_____

_____

3. What is the effect of severing the corpus callosum upon learning and bilateral transfer?_____

_____

_____

_____

4. In rats, what are the effects of (a) amount, and (b) location of cortical damage on learning?

    a. amount of damage_____

    _____

    b. location of damage_____

    _____

5. Relate the phenomenon of stimulus generalization to positive and negative transfer._____

_____

_____

Objectives

Be able to describe the various methods for
measuring memory and forgetting. Be able to des-
scribe the effects of the following on memory:
meaningfulness, association value, interpolated
activities, nitrous oxide, electronconvulsive
shock, and overlearning.

Be able to relate the phenomena of amnesia,
repression, the Zeigarnik effect, retroactive
and proactive inhibition to memory. Be able to
relate theories of forgetting to short-term
memory, long-term memory, the memory trace and
consolidation.

Define:

1. theory of disuse_____

_____

2. memory trace_____

_____

3. proactive inhibition_____

_____

4. retroactive inhibition_____

_____

5. overlearning_____

_____

6. mnemonic device_____

_____

7. clustering (in free recall)_____

_____

8. repression_____

_____

9. amnesia_____

_____

10. Zeigarnik effect_____

_____

11. RNA_____

_____

12. consolidation theory_____

_____

Questions:

1. What are the three ways in which memory is measured? Give an example
of each.

a._____

_____

_____

b._____

_____

_____

c._____

_____

_____

2. How does each of the following affect memory?

a. rehearsal_____

_____

b. overlearning_____

_____

c. nitrous oxide_____

_____

d. association value of nonsense syllables_____

_____

e. meaningfulness of material learned_____

_____

f. interpolated material_____

_____

g. intervening activities_____

_____

h. electroconvulsive shock_____

_____

i. number of alternatives on a recognition test_____

_____

3. Fill in the diagram below:

Proactive Inhibition

	Preceding Activity	Original learning	Test
Control group	unrelated activity	learn A	Recall A
Experimental group			

Retroactive Inhibition

	Original learning	Interpolated activity	Test
Control group	Learn A	Unrelated activity	Recall A
Experimental group			

4. Relate the Zeigarnik effect to repression_____

_____

_____

5. Relate short-term memory, long-term memory, and the consolidation theory._____

_____

_____

6. What data indicate that the theory of disuse in incorrect?_____

_____

_____

_____

7. What is the real reason for what most people commonly call "forgetting"?

_____

_____

_____

Objectives

Be able to tell how classical conditioning and
operant (instrumental) conditioning procedures and
phenomena are applied to verbal behavior. Be able
to tell how verbal behavior (semantic generalization
and word association) changes with age. Be able to
show how various areas of the brain relate to different types of amphasia.

Define:

1. phoneme _____
_____

2. semantic generalization _____
_____

3. antonym _____
_____

4. synonym _____
_____

5. homonym _____
_____

6. higher-order conditioning _____
_____

7. extensional meaning _____
_____

8. intensional meaning _____
_____

9. syntagmatic associates _____
_____

10. paradigmatic associates _____
_____

11. expressive aphasia _____
_____

12. receptive aphasia _____
_____

13. Broca's area _____
_____

Questions:

1. Relate the procedure of shaping to the development of language in a child._____

_____

_____

2. How does semantic generalization change with age?_____

_____

_____

_____

3. What type of conditioning could you use to attach a negative emotional response to a nonsense syllable? Describe the procedure in detail._____

_____

_____

4. How could higher-order conditioning attach a negative connotation to a word? How could this occur in a sentence?_____

_____

_____

5. What method of conditioning could you use to get a person to increase the rate of saying plural nouns? Describe the procedure used by Greenspoon (1955)._____

_____

_____

6. How do word associations change with age?_____

_____

_____

7. Which cerebal hemishphere is probably more important in the language behavior of a left-handed person?_____

a right-handed person?_____

8. Differentiate between expressive and receptive aphasia. What areas of the brain are important in each?_____

_____

_____

_____

Objectives

Be able to describe and define methods for studying symbolic behavior in animals and humans. Be able to describe the relationships among generalization, discrimination, and concept formation.

Be able to describe both reversal and nonreversal shifts, and their relationship to concept formation. Pay particular attention to the relationship between the complexity of the organism and the ease with which it can learn both types of shift. Be able to describe and relate the classes of complex concepts. Be able to discuss the major aspects of problem solving, including stages and specific methods of study.

State the purposes of computer simulation of cognitive processes and discuss the methods by which the study of information processing contributes to the understanding of cognitive processes.

Be able to describe the model of cognitive development presented by Jean Piaget.

Describe the roles of various areas of the brain and of the muscles in cognitive processes.

Define:

1. cognitive processes_____

_____

2. symbol_____

_____

3. delayed reaction method_____

_____

4. double alternation method_____

_____

5. concept learning_____

_____

6. reversal shift_____

_____

7. nonreversal shift_____

_____

8. conjunctive concept_____

_____

9. disjunctive concept_____

_____

10. relational concept_____

_____

11. habit competition_____

_____

12. detour problem_____

_____

13. functional fixedness_____

_____

14. set_____

_____

15. water-jar problem_____

_____

16. preparation_____

_____

17. incubation_____

_____

18. illumination_____

_____

19. verification_____

_____

20. general problem solver_____

_____

21. Jean Piaget_____

_____

22. frontal association area_____

_____

23. posterior association area_____

_____

Questions:

1. a. What methods are used to study symbolic behavior in animals?

   (1)_____

   _____

   (2)_____

   _____

   b. How do the following organisms do on the double alternation

   problem? (rank them)

   (1) rats_____   (3) monkeys_____

   (2) racoons_____   (4) humans_____

2. How are discrimination and concept learning related?_____

_____

_____

_____

3. a. Which do adult humans accomplish more easily, reversal or non-

   reversal shifts?_____

   b. What about rats?_____

   c. What about young children?_____

   How does this change as they grow older?_____

   _____

4. What are the three classes of complex concepts? Give an example of

each:

   a._____

   _____

   b._____

   _____

   c._____

   _____

5. What three phenomena demonstrate the importance of habit competition in problem solving? Give an example of each.

a._____

_____

b._____

_____

c._____

_____

6. What are the four successive stages of problem solving? (the order is important)

a._____

b._____

c._____

d._____

7. How is computer simulation used to study information processing and cognitive processes? Give both a general overview and specific examples.

_____

_____

8. Describe each of the four main stages of cognitive development.

a._____

b._____

c._____

d._____

9. Summarize the available knowledge on the physiological bases of cognitive processes._____

_____

_____

Objectives

Be able to define and differentiate between
a frustration situation, a state of frustration,
and a response to frustration. Be able to define
and interrelate the types of responses of frustra-
ion outlined in this unit.

Be able to discuss the relationship between
schedules of reinforcement, extinction, and frustration, and between stimulus generalization and
displacement.

Be able to describe the relationship between
frustration and fixation, and between punishment
and aggression, citing appropriate studies.

Define:

1. frustrating situation _____

_____

2. state of frustration _____

_____

3. response to frustration _____

_____

4. aggression _____

_____

5. displaced aggression _____

_____

6. apathy _____

_____

7. rationalization _____

_____

8. fantasy _____

_____

9. compensation _____

_____

10. overcompensation _____

_____

11. sublimation _____

_____

12. regression _____

_____

13. fixation _____

_____

91

Questions:

1. Explain the three components of frustration.

   a._____

   b._____

   c._____

2. What are the three main sources of frustration?

   a._____

   b._____

   c._____

3. List the seven types of responses to frustration.

   a._____

   b._____

   c._____

   d._____

   e._____

   f._____

   g._____

4. What is the relationship between stimulus generalization and displaced aggression? How was this shown in Miller's experiment?_____

_____

_____

_____

5. Which schedule of reinforcement results in greater frustration during extinction? Why?_____

_____

_____

_____

92

6. What is the most frequent effect of punishment on aggression?_____

_____

_____

_____

7. Describe the Maier studies on fixated habits._____

_____

_____

_____

Objectives

Be able to define and compare the major types
of conflict outlined in this unit. Be able to discuss the concepts of slope, gradient and equilibrium.

Be able to discuss the physiological effects
of conflict, with particular reference to experiments
by Brady and Pavlov.

Be able to discuss the methods of reducing
conflict.

Be able to discuss Selye's concept of stress,
with particular emphasis on stages of adaptation.

Define:

1. approach-approach conflict_____

_____

2. avoidance-avoidance conflict_____

_____

3. approach-avoidance conflict_____

_____

4. gradient_____

_____

5. slope_____

_____

6. unstable equilibrium_____

_____

7. stable equilibrium_____

_____

8. temporal conflict_____

_____

9. discrimination conflict_____

_____

10. Pavlov_____

_____

11. double approach-avoidance_____

_____

12. incompatable response method_____

_____

13. substitution method_____

_____

14. exhaustion method_____

_____

15. toleration method_____

_____

16. change-of-cue method_____

_____

17. general adaptation syndrome_____

_____

18. Selye_____

_____

19. stressors_____

_____

20. alarm reaction_____

_____

21. stage of resistance_____

_____

22. stage of exhaustion_____

_____

23. "executive monkey"_____

_____

24. Brady_____

_____

Questions:

1. What are Miller's principles of conflict?

   a._____

   _____

   b._____

   _____

   c._____

   _____

   d._____

   _____

   e._____

   _____

   f._____

   _____

2. What kinds of equilibrium are generated by:

   a. approach-approach conflict_____

   b. avoidance-avoidance conflict_____

   c. approach-avoidance conflict_____

3. Be able to explain how strengthening or weakening either gradient
in an approach-avoidance conflict will change an organism's behavior
toward the goal._____

_____

_____

_____

_____

4. What are the effects of alcohol and sodium amytal on the approach-avoidance conflict? How are these effects explained?_____

_____

_____

_____

_____

5. Summarize Pavlov's findings on discrimination conflict._____

_____

_____

_____

_____

6. What are the stages of Selye's General Adaptation Syndrome (in order)? Explain them.

a._____

_____

b._____

_____

c._____

_____

7. Describe Brady's "executive monkey" experiment.

a. What did the "executives" do?_____

_____

b. What did the controls do?_____

_____

c. Did the controls get more shocks (or less) than the executives?

_____

d. What were the results?_____

_____

e. What schedule did the "executives" work on?_____

_____

f. What happens if that schedule is changed?_____

_____

                          Objectives

     Understand Freud's ideas on the "mind" and his
stages of psychosexual development, and Miller and
Dollard's ideas on the development of personality.
Describe the effects of stress in infancy, and
understand the infant-mother relationship according
to Harlow.

Define:

1. personality_____

_____

2. conscious_____

_____

3. preconscious_____

_____

4. unconscious_____

_____

5. id_____

_____

6. ego_____

_____

7. superego_____

_____

8. libido_____

_____

9. ambivalence_____

_____

10. repression_____

_____

11. phobia_____

_____

12. self-esteem_____

_____

13. maternal overprotection_____

_____

14. sibling rivalry_____

_____

Questions:

1. What are the Freudian psychosexual stages of development? What
occurs in each stage?

a._____

_____

_____

b._____

_____

_____

c._____

_____

_____

d._____

_____

_____

2. Relate ambivalence and approach-avoidance conflicts._____

_____

_____

3. What is the greatest defect of Freud's theory?_____

_____

_____

4. List and explain the four situations stressed by Miller and Dollard
in the shaping of personality.

a._____

_____

b._____

_____

c._____

_____

d._____

_____

5. Relate self-esteem and response-produced cues._____

_____

_____

6. What situations develop high and low self-esteem?_____

_____

_____

_____

7. List and explain the four stages of the infant-mother relationship according to Harlow.

a._____

_____

b._____

_____

c._____

_____

d._____

_____

8. What are the effects of maternal deprivation on later behavior?___

_____

_____

9. What is the effect of mild stress in infancy? Severe stress?_____

_____

_____

_____

_____

Objectives

Be able to describe and give example of each
method of measuring personality. Understand reliability and validity. Be able to discuss the
concept of the personality trait. Be able to
describe the various efforts to understand personality on a physiological level.

Define:

1. interview method_____

_____

2. rating scales_____

_____

3. reliability_____

_____

4. validity_____

_____

5. halo effect_____

_____

6. personality inventory_____

_____

7. MMPI_____

_____

8. personality profile_____

_____

9. trait_____

_____

10. primary trait_____

_____

11. projective techniques_____

_____

12. Rorschach test_____

_____

13. TAT _____

_____

14. sentence completion test _____

_____

15. situational tests _____

_____

16. transfer of training _____

_____

17. psychogenetics _____

_____

18. thyroxin _____

_____

19. cretinism _____

_____

20. reserpine _____

_____

21. endomorph _____

_____

22. mesomorph _____

_____

23. ectomorph _____

_____

24. Sheldon _____

_____

Questions:

1. What are the four methods for assessing personality? Which is most
widely used?

     a._____

     b._____

     c._____

     d._____

2. Compare and contrast reliability and validity._____

_____

_____

_____

3. What are the difficulties with the Rorschach test? Compare it to
the TAT and MMPI._____

_____

_____

_____

4. Relate transfer of training to situational tests._____

_____

_____

_____

5. What types of behavior seem to be genetically determined in rats?

_____

_____

_____

_____

6. Describe the effects of reserpine on the following:

    a. overall rate of responding_____

    _____

    b. responding during a fear-evoking stimulus_____

    _____

7. Describe Sheldon's theory. How valid is it?_____

_____

_____

_____

Objectives

Be able to define and distinguish among the
major behavioral disorders outlined in this unit.
Be able to match the clinical classifications with
their associated behaviors.

Be able to distinguish functional from organic
disorders, psychosomatic reactions from conversion
reactions, obsession from compulsion, phobia from
anxiety reaction. Be able to discuss Dollard and
Miller's description of neurotic behavior and the
role of learning in psychopathology.

Define:

1. adjustment_____

_____

2. neurosis_____

_____

3. anxiety reaction_____

_____

4. free-floating anxiety_____

_____

5. phobic reaction_____

_____

6. obsessions_____

_____

7. compulsions_____

_____

8. conversion reactions_____

_____

9. hysterical sensory disturbances_____

_____

10. hysterical paralyses_____

_____

11. hysterical motor disturbances_____

_____

12. dissociative reaction_____

_____

13. amnesia_____

_____

14. fugue_____

_____

15. multiple personality_____

_____

16. depressive reactions_____

_____

17. psychosomatic reactions_____

_____

18. ulceration_____

_____

Questions:

1. What problems are there with the various definitions of "mental health"?_____

_____

_____

_____

2. What are Miller and Dollard's three criteria for neuroticism?

    a._____

    b._____

    c._____

3. Relate fear and anxiety_____

_____

_____

_____

4. What are the roles of classical conditioning and stimulus generalization in phobias?_____

_____

_____

5. How are obsessive-compulsive reactions reinforced? Conversion
reactions?_____

_____

_____

_____

6. How are conversion and psychosomatic reactions different?_____

_____

_____

_____

113

7. How do Miller's experiments (on heart rate) bear upon the origins

of psychosomatic reactions?_____

_____

_____

_____

Objectives

Be able to define and distinguish among the
various psychoses and character disorders. Be
able to distinguish among the four types of schizophrenia outlined in this unit with particular reference to the defining characteristics of each.
Be able to discuss the relationship between drugs
and behavior with particular reference to LSD and
alcohol. Be able to describe the major causes of
organic psychosis. Be able to distinguish between
psychopaths and sociopaths, between hypermania
and hypomania, between organic and functional
psychosis. Be able to discuss the relationship
between fear reduction and alcholism.

Define:

1. psychosis (plural, psychoses)_____

_____

2. schizophrenia_____

_____

3. simple type_____

_____

4. paranoid type_____

_____

5. delusions of persecution_____

_____

6. hebephrenic type_____

_____

7. catatonic type_____

_____

8. waxy flexibility_____

_____

9. LSD_____

_____

10. manic-depressive reaction_____

_____

11. hypermania_____

_____

12. hypomania_____

_____

13. involutional malancholia_____

_____

14. paresis_____

_____

15. delirium tremens_____

_____

16. senile psychosis_____

_____

17. Korsakow's syndrome_____

_____

18. character disorder_____

_____

19. psychopath_____

_____

20. sociopath_____

_____

Questions:

1. What are the two main classes of psychoses? How do they differ?__

_____

_____

_____

_____

2. What are the probable causes of schizophrenia?_____

_____

_____

3. Differentiate between hypomania and hypermania_____

_____

_____

_____

4. What are the four major causes of organic psychoses?

     a._____

     b._____

     c._____

     d._____

Objectives

Be able to describe and distinguish among the major therapeutic approaches discussed in this unit. State the rationale behind each. Be able to discuss the major divisions within the therapies in this unit, i.e.: under behavior modification--behavior therapy, aversion therapy, shaping therapy, etc.

Be able to distinguish between nondirective and directive approaches to therapy. Be able to relate the therapeutic approaches discussed in this unit to the behavioral pathology for which each is appropriate. Cite appropriate comparative studies.

Define:

1. psychotherapy_____

_____

2. somatotherapy_____

_____

3. psychoanalysis_____

_____

4. free association_____

_____

5. transference_____

_____

6. client-centered therapy_____

_____

7. non-directive therapy_____

_____

8. behavior modification (behavior therapy)_____

_____

9. desensitization therapy_____

_____

10. aversion therapy_____

_____

11. shaping therapy_____

_____

12. autism_____

_____

13. group therapy_____

_____

14. psychodrama_____

_____

15. insulin shock therapy_____

_____

16. electroshock therapy (ECS)_____

_____

17. chemotherapy_____

_____

18. reserpine_____

_____

19. shaping_____

_____

20. secondary reinforcement_____

_____

Questions:

1. What is the basis of psychoanalysis?_____

_____

_____

_____

2. What is the main task of the client-centered therapist?_____

_____

_____

_____

3. In what way do behavior therapists disagree with the "disease" concept of mental illness?_____

_____

_____

4. Relate the following concepts:

    a. desensitization, extinction, habit competition_____

    _____

    _____

    b. aversion therapy, punishment, fear_____

    _____

    _____

    c. shaping therapy, positive reinforcement, successive approximations, autism_____

    _____

    _____

5. Describe the experiment by Paul on anxiety and public speaking. Which therapeutic method worked best?_____

_____

_____

6. In which psychosis is electroshock therapy most effective? What
are its drawbacks?_____

_____

_____

_____

7. Relate the findings of the reserpine experiment in Unit 23 to
chemotherapy. What implications do they have?_____

_____

_____

_____

Objectives

Understand the general process of socialization
and how social class functions in the socialization
of children. Be able to describe factors which relate to the social development of black children.

Understand communication networks and the effects
of group structure. Be able to discuss the factors
which affect leadership.

Define:

1. socialization_____

_____

2. shaping_____

_____

3. culture_____

_____

4. subculture_____

_____

5. need for achievement_____

_____

6. social role_____

_____

7. relative deprivation_____

_____

8. social dyad_____

_____

9. communication network_____

_____

10. "wheel"_____

_____

11. "circle"_____

_____

12. centralized_____

_____

125

13. decentralized_____

_____

14. sociogram_____

_____

15. democratic group structure_____

_____

16. autocratic group structure_____

_____

17. "consideration"_____

_____

18. "initiating structure"_____

_____

Questions:

1. How do changes in sources of reinforcement occur as children develop?

_____

_____

_____

2. When is punishment effective in socializing a child?_____

_____

_____

3. How do the following behaviors differ in the lower vs. middle class?

    a. need for achievement_____

    _____

    b. value academic success_____

    _____

    c. use positive reinforcement to shape child_____

    _____

    d. use severe punishment to train child_____

    _____

    e. psychotic behavior_____

    _____

    f. work for internal sources of reinforcement_____

    _____

4. List a number of factors that probably are responsible for the
relatively low academic performance of black children.

    a._____

    b._____

    c._____

    d._____

e._____

5. Which combination of factors would result in the worst performance

in a black child: white or black tester, using approval or disapproval?

_____

_____

   Which combination would yield the best performance?_____

_____

6. List factors that may be responsible for racial conflict (e.g. Watts):

   a._____

   b._____

   c._____

   d._____

   e._____

7. List some advantages and disadvantages of these communication net-

works:

   a. "wheel"_____

   _____

   b. "circle"_____

   _____

8. According to the book, what effects do group structures have on

productivity? (describe the study)._____

_____

_____

9. Analysis of supervisor's behavior would reveal what two factors that

are responsible for success?_____

_____

_____

Objectives

Be able to explain the relationship among
attitudes, beliefs, and values, and the variables
that influence attitudes. Thoroughly understand
the assumptions of cognitive dissonance theory
and the studies that support it. Understand
conformity and the variable that influence it.

Define:

1. attitude_____

_____

2. belief_____

_____

3. value_____

_____

4. rating scale_____

_____

5. classical conditioning_____

_____

6. ethnocentrism_____

_____

7. authoritarianism_____

_____

8. social environment_____

_____

9. cognitive dissonance_____

_____

10. conformity_____

_____

Questions:

1. What is the relationship between attitudes, beliefs, and values?

_____

_____

_____

2. How can classical conditioning be used to change attitudes? Give an example._____

_____

_____

3. What behaviors does the ethnocentric person typically exhibit?____

_____

_____

4. How do the following affect attitudes?

    a. motivation and reinforcement_____

_____

    b. social environment_____

_____

    c. personality_____

_____

5. What are the three assumptions of cognitive dissonance theory?

    a._____

_____

    b._____

_____

    c._____

_____

6. Describe the following studies:

   a. Festinger and Carlsmith ($1 vs $20 study)_____

   _____

   _____

   b. Aronson and Mills (initiation study)_____

   _____

   _____

   c. Aronson and Carlsmith (toy study)_____

   _____

   _____

   d. Asch (conformity study)_____

   _____

   e. Milgram (shock study)_____

   _____

   _____

7. What effects do the prestige and credibility of the communicator
have upon the persuasiveness of messages?_____

_____

_____

8. What are the group variables that influence conformity?

   a._____

   b._____

   c._____

   d._____

Objectives

Be able to distinguish between achievement and
aptitude tests and be able to describe the characteristics of a useful test. Be able to describe
and differentiate between the different intelligence
and aptitude tests describe in this unit.

Be able to compute an I.Q. score. Be able to
describe the interaction between hereditary and en-
vironmental determinants of intelligence with reference to the data on twins and the data on racial
differences. Be able to discuss mental retardation
and the difference between "gifted" and "genius".

Define:

1. aptitude test _____

_____

2. validity _____

_____

3. critical score _____

_____

4. false positive _____

_____

5. false negative _____

_____

6. achievement test _____

_____

7. operational definition _____

_____

8. Stanford-Binet _____

_____

9. mental age _____

_____

10. chronological age _____

_____

11. I.Q. _____

_____

12. WAIS _____

_____

13. AGCT_____

_____

14. culture-free tests_____

_____

15. mental retardation_____

_____

16. phenylketonuria (PKU)_____

_____

17. Down's syndrome_____

_____

18. general intelligence_____

_____

19. specific intelligence_____

_____

20. factor analysis_____

_____

Questions:

1. How reliable are I.Q. test scores? What is the average range of
test scores _for_ _an_ _individual?_____

_____

_____

2. What is the mean and standard deviation of the I.Q. distribution
for _the_ _general_ _population?_

_____

_____

3. How do intelligence test scores change with age?_____

_____

_____

_____

4. How does environment influence intelligence test scores?_____

_____

_____

_____

5. What are the data concerning the role of heredity in influencing
intelligence?_____

_____

_____

6. What conclusion can be drawn concerning racial genetic differences
in intelligence?_____

_____

_____

_____

7. What enviromental factors may account for racial differences in intelligence test scores?_____

_____

_____

8. What is the usual cut-off I.Q. for the classification of "mildly re-tarded"?_____

9. List the factors that may cause retardation.

    a._____

    b._____

    c._____

10. Distinguish between "gifted" and "genius"._____

_____

_____

_____

11. What physical and emotional characteristics do "gifted" people have?

_____

_____

_____

12. What characteristics make a psychological test useful?

    a._____

    _____

    b._____

    _____

    c._____

    _____

Objectives
Be able to understand the various aspects of
human engineering. Be able to relate shaping to
programmed instruction and understand the five
principles involved. Be able to tell the features
and functions of the various vocational tests.

Define:

1. human engineering_____

_____

2. man-machine system_____

_____

3. aligned and non-aligned displays_____

_____

4. stimulus-response compatability_____

_____

5. antoinstructional device_____

_____

6. program_____

_____

7. shaping_____

_____

8. prompting_____

_____

9. formal prompt_____

_____

10. thematic prompt_____

_____

11. vanishing technique_____

_____

12. linear programming_____

_____

13. branching programming_____

_____

14. scrambled textbook_____

_____

15. ruleg system _____

_____

16. computer assisted instruction_____

_____

Questions:

1. Relate the concepts of stimulus generalization and negative transfer to the design of displays and the design of controls._____

_____

_____

_____

2. What are the effects of the following on performance? Give examples.

    a. sensory "overloading"_____

_____

    b. sensory "underloading"_____

_____

3. What is the basic learning process underlying programmed instruction?

_____

4. Give and explain the five principles of programmed instruction

    a._____

_____

    b._____

_____

    c._____

_____

    d._____

_____

    e._____

_____

5. Why does Skinner feel that recall items are more appropriate than recognition items in a program?_____

_____

6. Distinguish between the ruleg system and the inductive method._____

_____

_____

7. What are the advantages and disadvantages of educational films?___

_____

_____

_____

8. List the distinctive features, assumptions, and uses of each test:

    a. Strong Vocational interest test_____

    _____

    _____

    b. Kuder Preference Record_____

    _____

    _____

    c. Differential Aptitude test_____

    _____

    _____